Josephine's Journey ~

A BREAST CANCER SURVIVOR'S STORY OF HOPE

by

Josephine M. Roach, PA, MS

To Kimberly
Maintain FAITH
and HOPE
throughout life.
♡ Josephine
2022

Josephine's Journey -
A BREAST CANCER SURVIVOR'S STORY OF HOPE
By Josephine M. Roach, PA, MS

Cover Graphic Design: Patricia Laurenceau

Cover Photograph: Josephine M. Roach

Editor: Gloria Palmer (movinonup57@yahoo.com)

ISBN: 978-0-9985511-3-5

Contact the Author: Josephine M. Roach, PA, MS
                         josephineroach11@gmail.com

DEDICATION

In honor of my dear Mamma Antonetta,
who taught me the true meaning of
love, strength, and perseverance.

Nessuno muore finché ne rimane la memoria.
Ti voglio bene, mamma.

Acknowledgements

Thank you to Jim, my husband, who walked beside me during this challenging, life-changing journey. I appreciate your encouragement and love.

Thank you to Dr. Anita Caprice (Artist Angel) for driving me forward in my dreams by inspiring me to create my Zoom Series, *Journey & Journal with Josephine*, which led to the writing of this book.

Thank you to my friend Eileen Burns. She served as an excellent resource person during this book writing project.

Thank you to William Kern and Paula Kaye, photographers extraordinaire and friends, for their experience and talent in enhancing the photograph for my book cover. I wanted my book cover to have a special meaning. As you will read in Chapter 4 of my first journal entry, while I was on my way to see the breast surgeon, I was stopped at a traffic light. I looked up at the sky and saw rays of sunshine, shining straight paths of light through the fluffy clouds. The sight filled me with hope, so I captured it with my camera. You are seeing what I saw that very day on the cover of this book.

Thank you to all those survivors, fighters, thrivers, and warriors who keep me going. Each time I speak to one of you, I am humbled and understand the meaning and purpose behind writing this book.

CONTENTS

Josephine's Journey ~

A BREAST CANCER SURVIVOR'S STORY OF HOPE

FOREWORD

I first met Josephine in the summer of 2018, as she was nearing the end of her treatment journey. I remember the visit vividly: her silver-gray bob, her bright lip color, her notebook and pen. I remember her pert, alert expression, her sharp way of holding my gaze. She dressed conservatively and was composed and articulate. One could have easily missed her suffering, but the diagnosis of breast cancer and exposure to treatment had unsettled her in so many ways. The least of these were the physical impacts.

Josephine is a survivor, but her book is less about survivorship than it is about what she went through, not just to survive but to thrive. She carried other tools in her toolbox: her wish to advocate for others and herself, righteous anger, and hope.

Josephine highlights her desire to find the right team of clinicians and support staff in her cancer journey and her need to trust in her providers' skills, expertise, and transparency. She ultimately found the healthcare team that was right for her.

Associates of Integrative Medicine is one of two integrative oncology practices in Michigan that staffs nationally-board-certified supportive care oncology providers. I am one of only approximately eighty "naturopathic" oncologists in the United States and Canada. This makes us hard to find. But find us, Josephine did. One of the most important roles we play in patient care is the prevention of dose-limiting side effects, so patients can tolerate the drugs and feel well.

A cancer diagnosis forces us to ask the questions Josephine talks about in this book: Who am I? Am I beautiful? Am I strong? Is my beauty something outside of me? What do I value the most? Am I important to others? Is my marriage true to the vows we took? Can I stand in my faith? What is the purpose of my life?

Josephine spoke *honestly* about how she approached these questions, and one thing she writes with great courage about is her anger. We saddle anger with negative attributes, but it can be a kinetic force for change. Giving voice to her anger, finding a way to express it safely, and feeling heard was a motivating force for Josephine.

Anger for Josephine is married to hope.

"Hope is the thing with feathers that perches in the soul, And sings the tune without the words, And never stops at all," wrote Emily Dickinson. I see this book as Josephine's song, her clear tune to help others who hear the words, "You have cancer," to do better than even she did. And, most importantly, for them to be empowered to do as she did: Hold her own life in her hands; use the rage of powerlessness, hurt, and impotence to move forward; and nourish hope that her suffering is a gift for others.

This book is special, personal, and essential. I hope you enjoy it as I did. I pray that Josephine's courage in allowing us a glimpse into her deepest fears, hurts, and triumphs inspires us to continue finding the transformation that this disease can offer.

God Bless and Be Well,

Sheba Roy, ND FABNO
Clinical Director, Associates of Integrative Medicine
Detroit, Michigan

INTRODUCTION

A cancer diagnosis shakes you. I looked at life much differently after being diagnosed with breast cancer. As I reflected on all I had gone through in my journey, I knew I had a story to tell. I had experienced a rollercoaster of emotions, some so new to me, and I learned so much about myself and from the many people I met. This book will be beneficial if you are recently diagnosed, in treatment, a survivor, a co-survivor, or know someone who is. My desire is that you will connect with the many emotions of a cancer diagnosis and learn from some of the things I encountered.

I journaled through my journey, writing how I felt each step of the way. There was the biopsy appointment, the doctor consultations, second opinions, surgeries, tests, and treatments. Through it all, I maintained hope. Hope was something I hung onto when there was nothing else. I hoped for brighter days. I prayed for those diagnosed before me and those diagnosed after me. I prayed they would fight and conquer cancer. And, I hope someday there is a cure.

I found journaling to be very therapeutic as I went through my journey. It helped me work through my feelings and let me release some of the emotional pain I endured. It enabled me to focus. I often journaled after a doctor's appointment or treatment. I received important information during my appointments and made sure I wrote it down in a safe place that I could reference later. If you are currently on your cancer journey, I encourage you to journal. It is a handy tool to store in your toolbox and bring out to help you sort out all that is happening at this most difficult time of your life.

Many people crossed my path during my journey for reasons that are so clear to me now. You will meet some of these remarkable people in the pages that follow. If it had not been for these compassionate, knowledgeable, caring, and loving individuals, my story and how I viewed a breast cancer diagnosis would have been much different. I certainly could not have gone through this without countless people. Support is so important when you are diagnosed with cancer. The many phone calls, daily text messages, cards, gifts—some from people I did not even know—made me realize what I meant to people. Yes, believe it or not, cancer taught me how important I was to others. That is one of the silver linings of my story. There is life after cancer, and I am using that life to help educate others about breast cancer. It is my time to shine after the dark days I encountered.

Throughout it all, my message to you is this: *Get your yearly mammogram; it could save your life.* It saved mine. If I help just one person achieve this, it will fulfill the purpose of writing this book. My name is Josephine. Come along with me as I take you through my breast cancer journey and journal.

CHAPTER 1
GOD'S PLAN

Where do I go from here? My life needs more balance. I had been caring for my mother for the past eleven years after she suffered a debilitating stroke. It was a difficult job, but one I would not have changed because I was giving back to her in some small way for the excellent care she had given to me as a mother. Being her healthcare advocate and ensuring she received good care was my goal. She always came first in my life. The bond between mother and daughter strengthened during this time spent together. The love I have for her is immeasurable.

Being one of my mother's caregivers taught me many lessons, which I am grateful for today. While caring for her, I realized the fragility of life and how it can change instantly. I learned not to take anything or anyone for granted. My mother showed me the true meaning of strength and perseverance through her health struggles. These crucial lessons served me well later in my own life. However, after eleven years of caregiving, I felt I needed more in my life; something was missing. That's when I started thinking about volunteer work. I was looking into some volunteer programs in various healthcare systems because I had previously worked as a Physician Assistant (PA). Healthcare and advocacy were my interests. I thought that would be an excellent avenue to pursue.

I was getting ready to meet my good friend Yvette for dinner one evening and thought of discussing my new endeavor with her. It was a cold November evening, and I welcomed meeting my dear friend. We met at one of our favorite restaurants, sat at the front booth window seat, and began to catch up. Yvette was a PA I had met years ago when I'd decided to become a PA myself. She was gracious enough to let me job shadow her in Family Practice. Then later, she mentored me as I pursued my Master of Science degree in Physician Assistant Studies at the University of Detroit Mercy. We became fast friends, and I often turned to her for advice.

I told her I was searching for more balance in my life and thinking about volunteer work. Yvette immediately directed me to someone she knew who volunteered at Komen Detroit Race for the Cure, and said, in fact, I might know her as well. Her name was Jan, and we all attended the same church. Yvette thought Jan would be a good contact for me. She told me to give her a call and she might be able to help. I thought, *'What an excellent opportunity to be able to help women and men with breast cancer—what a worthy cause.'*

I left our dinner feeling invigorated and eager to call Jan. It is interesting how God sets you out on your life path for reasons you may not realize until much later.

CHAPTER 2
KOMEN DETROIT RACE FOR THE CURE VOLUNTEER

I called Jan that next day. She was kind and willing to help me with volunteering at Komen Detroit Race for the Cure. She suggested I call her friend Sandy who chaired the Teams Committee for the Race.

Sandy was a ball of energy, a breast cancer survivor who welcomed me. She was looking for volunteers to help with her Committee. The Teams Committee oversees the teams participating on Race Day. These included family teams, friends, church groups, school organizations, and businesses. The Committee also makes sure these groups are on track with fundraising. They organize packet pick up, where a team needs to pick up their Race T-shirts for Race Day. It sounded like a lot of work, but I was up for the challenge. She also mentioned they were looking for a writer for their monthly newsletter. She invited me to attend the first Komen Detroit Planning Committee Meeting for the 2013 Race and extended an invitation to the Teams Committee Meeting at her home. I was thrilled to meet these wonderful people and begin my volunteer experience!

Everyone was so friendly and inviting at the Teams Committee meeting. This Race they were talking about sounded like quite the event. I had never attended a Race of this magnitude. There were as many as twenty-five thousand people in attendance in Races past! I met Mo Keenan Meldrum that night. She was the Komen Detroit Race for the Cure Chair and Director of Breast Cancer Special Programs at Karmanos Cancer Institute. What a dynamic woman! Her passion for this cause shined. She had done so much for the breast cancer community and it was an honor to meet her. She was also a breast cancer survivor who had tremendous insight and a calm way of talking about such a scary disease. After meeting everyone and learning about the Komen Detroit Race for the Cure, I immediately felt this was exactly the place for me.

That was the beginning of a volunteer experience that continues to this day. I became the writer for the monthly Teams newsletter Sandy had mentioned in our first conversation. I went on to Chair the Teams Committee when Sandy moved to Arizona. What started as a small volunteer experience grew into a much bigger one with a leadership role.

Each year I attended the Komen Detroit Race for the Cure, a particular portion of the Opening Ceremonies touched me: When the Honor Guard paraded onto the stage, many emotions filled me. The Honor Guard consists of people representing those living with metastatic disease and those who are under-one-year, one-year, five-year, ten-year, fifteen-year, twenty-year, twenty-five-year, and thirty-year breast cancer survivors—strong individuals who are living with breast cancer or who have survived this terrible disease. They are doing it with grace, dignity, and courage. It brought tears to my eyes each year. Little did I know when I was embracing those special moments and watching those brave people walk up onto that stage, I would soon become one of them.

CHAPTER 3
MY YEARLY MAMMOGRAM

It was September 2017, and I made my yearly mammogram appointment. I scheduled it for the end of the month. I went to the appointment, not thinking there would be any problems. I even posted on Facebook that I was there and to make sure to get your yearly mammogram. At this point, I had begun sharing my thoughts on breast cancer, and breast cancer advocacy had become very important to me because of my volunteer experience. I was now meeting people living with a breast cancer diagnosis or who were survivors. Many of the people on the Komen Detroit Planning Committee were survivors themselves.

Once at my appointment, I got into that awful stiff gown they give you. You have to tie it in the front, like a robe. If you are busty, like me, you never feel entirely covered. As I sat in the brightly-lit waiting room, I looked at the other women. Seated in front of me was a petite, middle-aged woman with long, dark, cascading hair partially covering her small face. In her hand, she was gripping a prayer card. As I turned to my right, I saw a woman with round blue eyes. Her gaze was fixed and distant.

Fear, an emotion so real and so raw, certainly can occur on mammogram day. I admit now that I was a bit nervous and uncomfortable, but I had been through this numerous times without any issues. The mammographer called me back, and I went through the uncomfortable but necessary process. When they flatten out your breast to what seems to be the point of a pancake, it hurts! It only lasts momentarily though, then on to the other breast. I mentioned to the mammogram tech that I was a volunteer for the Komen Detroit Race for the Cure. I asked if she had ever participated and if she would like to form a team. I was always trying to bring people into the Race, especially those connected to breast cancer.

After she finished, she asked me to return to a nearly-empty waiting room. I sat there until an ultrasound technologist came to get me and brought me into her exam room. She explained that the radiologist had seen something on my right breast on the mammogram and wanted some different views using ultrasound. I had done this before, so I was not too concerned. The ultrasound is much more comfortable than the mammogram. I lay on an exam table and warm ultrasound gel was placed on my breast. I looked at the screen as she went over certain areas.

After she finished, I returned to a now-empty waiting room. Sitting there, I thought it was taking an unusually long time. Finally, a nurse called my name. In the past, she would say, "Everything looks good; you will get a letter in the mail with your negative results. We will see you next year." Not so today. The nurse asked me to follow her and escorted me into an office. At that moment, I knew something was terribly wrong. She told me the radiologist had seen something suspicious on my mammogram and ultrasound. I needed to return for a core needle breast biopsy to determine what they had seen on these imaging tests.

I left the hospital dazed and got into my car. Shocked, I sat in the driver's seat. How could this be happening to me? My mind jumped to the worst-case scenario. As I drove home, tears streamed down my face. I felt lost and needed to call and tell someone. But instead, I called no one, went home, and sat on the couch in my living room, alone, waiting for my husband to return from work to tell him the news.

My husband, Jim, is a very calm, positive, methodical man who has worked as an engineer for over thirty years. He never jumps to conclusions or worst-case scenarios like I do. He was lucky enough to marry a passionate, spitfire Italian girl! His reaction was just as I suspected, saying to wait until we knew the final result. Why worry about something that hasn't happened yet? Yep, he was right, but I knew women who'd had to get breast biopsies in the past, and they'd experienced the same anxiety I was feeling. It was at that moment I began writing in my journal. I had always journaled throughout my life. It helped me collect my thoughts and organize my feelings. This event certainly needed to be documented.

Chapter 4
The Breast Biopsy

I scheduled an appointment with a breast surgeon. He was to explain the breast biopsy procedure to me. I felt nervous driving to that appointment. As I was stopped at a traffic light, I looked up at the sky. I recorded in my journal later that day what I saw and felt at that very moment.

September 25, 2017

> I saw a beautiful sun through the clouds today. I saw the rays of sunshine shining straight paths of light through the light, fluffy clouds. It came at just the right time. God is good, and He was sending me a message that **HE** is with me **ALWAYS**. Do not forget to call on God for strength and to ask for help. Papa, help me and be by my side today.

I remember this day vividly. I remember the street I was driving on. If I close my eyes, I can still see the sun streaming through the clouds and remember calling on my faith and knowing my father, who has passed, was by my side. I could feel his comfort and support. At that moment, I thought, 'This must be where HOPE begins.'

My medical background as a Physician Assistant served me well. At the appointment, I sat before the surgeon, and the first question I asked him was what was the BI-RADS score of my mammogram. Now a layperson may not know about this score, but I did. It is a scoring system radiologists use to describe mammogram results. The score suggests the likelihood of a lesion being cancerous or not. He said the BI-RADS score was low, and I should **NOT** be worried. He went on to explain the biopsy procedure to me. I scheduled the breast biopsy for two weeks later, which felt like a lifetime.

October 10, 2017 – Biopsy Day

This biopsy procedure sure did not turn out to be what I thought. The interventional radiologist I had was filling in from an affiliated hospital, which made me nervous. She had to go quite deep with the fine needle into my right breast, which was very uncomfortable. Once she got the sample, they had to tag the area and do a mammogram to ensure they had biopsied the correct spot. I was to wait to make sure everything was okay before I left. To my surprise, the radiologist came out and said she wanted me to come back and look at my mammograms. She had the previous year's mammogram up alongside the current mammogram. She apologized and said, "I biopsied the wrong area. See your mammogram from last year; this appears to be a fibroadenoma (a noncancerous, benign area); that's what I biopsied. That appears to be stable. I am concerned about what is up here on this year's mammogram". I will never forget what the area looked like she was showing me. She asked, "Can you stay so I can biopsy that area?" My head was spinning. What had just happened? Of course, I could stay.

Afterward, I raced home to Google "breast cancer on a mammogram", and what I saw horrified me. It looked very similar to the white splotch on my upper, inner right breast she had shown me on my mammogram. I felt sick to my stomach. I knew right then, without anyone telling me, that I had breast cancer.

CHAPTER 5
A LIFE-CHANGING CALL

On the morning of October 12, 2017, my husband and I planned a weekend trip up to Petoskey, Michigan. That morning before we left, I stood in the kitchen, looking at him, and said, "Jim, I think I have breast cancer." Of course, he said all the right things to reassure me. We were going away and he said, "Let's concentrate on this nice weekend." I thought, okay, but I was still fearful. I just kept thinking about that picture I'd Googled online of how breast cancer looked on a mammogram. I could not get that image out of my mind.

We started on our way to Petoskey, and about twenty minutes into our drive, I received a phone call from the nurse at the breast surgeon's office. My stomach began churning as I listened to her. The nurse said direct and short, "Your biopsy has come back positive for breast cancer." My heart was pounding out of my chest as Jim pulled over to the side of the road. I asked, "What stage?" She said, "It is most likely Stage I. Let's set up an appointment with the breast surgeon to discuss what the next steps will be." I was numb. I looked at Jim, and he knew my fear had come true. My life would be forever changed. It was one of the worst days of my life, one I will never forget.

I could not go up to Petoskey that day; I just couldn't. Jim turned the car around and we returned home. Jim got out of the car and went into the house, but I stayed sitting in the car alone. I was in disbelief. I remember calling my good friend Yvette who had gone through breast cancer. She was shocked but reassuring. Here we were, close friends, both diagnosed with breast cancer. If anyone knew what I was feeling at that moment, it was her.

I then called my brother to tell him the news. I was so scared. Telling my brother that his little sister had breast cancer was not easy. My brother John has a gentle way about him, and he did just that by comforting and calming me. Soon after the phone calls, my mind turned to what the breast surgeon had told me two weeks prior: "I should not be worried." What false hope he had given me.

I had a few days to digest the diagnosis. Then I felt anger as I questioned, "Why did the breast surgeon say that to me? What had gone wrong?" I wrote a list of questions for that surgeon, and I was ready to face him and what was to come.

October 19, 2017

I was ready with questions in hand for my appointment with the breast surgeon. Jim came with me, and I think we were both nervous. As we entered the exam room, my heart began to race and I needed to take some calming deep breaths. The surgeon entered the room after what seemed like an eternity. He shook our hands and sat down. "So, I want to go over the biopsy results once again and then talk about what we need to do moving forward." I stopped him dead in his tracks when I said, "We certainly are having a different conversation from when I saw you last, aren't we? You told me the probability of my breast lesion being cancer was low and that was not true." I paused to hear a response. To my amazement, he replied, "Kinda-sorta." I was dumbfounded. This surgeon, whom I was waiting on for a well-thought-out response, had replied with, "Kinda-

sorta," as an explanation. My blood started to boil. He quickly changed the subject and said, "Let's go into the consultation room to discuss the next steps." Sure, I thought, but I already knew I would be seeking a second opinion, and this surgeon was not going to touch me.

We continued into the consultation room. I had some questions, one being what was the type of tumor. The surgeon told me it was progesterone/estrogen positive, and **HER2-negative**. I was at least relieved to hear that it was HER2-negative because I was doing my research at home and knew that HER2-positive was a very aggressive cancer that would need much more treatment. He discussed I needed an MRI to determine the tumor's exact size and how deep it was in my chest. After receiving the MRI results, he said his nurse would set up a lumpectomy. He asked, "How does that sound?" I told him I was involved with Komen Detroit Race for the Cure, affiliated with the Karmanos Cancer Institute. I would be seeking a second opinion there. He said, "Of course," and that was the end of the appointment.

Jim and I left, and on the drive home, we were still in disbelief of the surgeon's use of "kinda-sorta". What kind of explanation was that? It seemed to me as a significant oversight in my mammogram.

I called my friend Laura the next day to see if she could recommend a breast surgeon at Karmanos Cancer Institute, where she worked. Laura served on the Komen Detroit Race for the Cure Planning Committee with me and I trusted her implicitly. When I asked her what she would do if she were me after explaining what had happened, she said, "Josephine, we are a cancer institute. All we do is cancer here. We are fortunate to have such an institute in our state. Why would you go anywhere else?" That was all I needed to hear. Those words of wisdom made me know that Karmanos Cancer Institute would be an excellent place to treat my breast cancer. Laura called me back within an hour and had an appointment set up with a female breast surgeon she thought would be a good fit for me. The appointment was set for the following week.

October 24, 2017 – Second Opinion

Jim and I went down to Karmanos Cancer Institute today. We met with a breast surgeon for a second opinion. I brought a copy of my mammogram and biopsy results and had the slides sent from the biopsy I had at the previous hospital. I had questions written down for her.

The surgeon entered the exam room, her demeanor calm. She spoke clearly and straightforwardly. She said she would have the radiologists look at my mammogram. I had expressed my concern that the other surgeon had said I needed an MRI to determine the size of the tumor. She left the room and returned with my mammogram and a report saying, "You do not need an MRI. Your mammogram has determined that the tumor size is approximately 1.7 cm. On the mammogram, you can see the tumor is going slightly into your chest muscle, so I will have to remove a little muscle along with the tumor."

The breast surgeon then explained where she would do the incisions and would have to remove several lymph nodes in my armpit. They needed to test for cancer there as well. She explained that she would try to obtain "clear margins" during the surgery, meaning no cancer cells at the outer edge of the tissue that would be removed. She went on to describe the "Oncotype DX Score". The higher this score, the more likely breast cancer will come back and the more likely you are to benefit from chemotherapy. She paused then said, "Think about what I have just said to you and give me a callback, or if you feel comfortable with what I have told you, we can schedule a surgery date today." She left the room.

I looked at Jim and said, "I like her. I do not need an MRI, as the other surgeon said. She determined the approximate size of my tumor by the mammogram and talked about getting clear margins and Oncotype DX Score, none of which the other surgeon had even mentioned." I decided I wanted to have this surgeon perform my surgery, and Jim agreed. She came back into the room, and I told her I wanted to move forward to have the lumpectomy with a sentinel node biopsy. She then had her scheduler come in, and I scheduled my surgery for November 10th, two weeks from today.

I want to stress a point here. Second opinions are always good, especially when facing a serious diagnosis like cancer. You may like the first doctor you encounter, which is also okay, but, by getting a second opinion, you can compare what each doctor presents to you. If it is the same, that's great. Then you decide which doctor is best for you. Some people even get third opinions when there appear to be discrepancies. I was worried about the time that was passing by getting other opinions. After the lumpectomy, the surgeon reassured me that we would have an oncologist talk to me about treatment. I was on a reasonable timetable from the initial mammogram to surgery.

BE YOUR OWN ADVOCATE. IT IS YOUR BODY, YOUR HEALTH, YOUR RIGHT. The doctors are working for you, so make the best decision for YOU. I did.

CHAPTER 6
I WILL SURVIVE!

It was the day of my lumpectomy. Jim and I got up at four a.m. to prepare and begin our one-hour drive to downtown Detroit. I had not slept much that night. My mind was going over everything that had occurred in the past month. How was it that now I was a breast cancer patient? I was the one who supported and helped those with breast cancer. A complete role reversal had transpired. I researched the surgery in depth. Being on the other side as a patient and not the healthcare provider was very scary.

When we arrived at the hospital, hardly anyone was in the sterile-looking waiting room. I filled out some paperwork, gave the receptionist my insurance card, and was called back to the pre-op area. Jim was able to be with me during this time. As I looked at him, I could see the fear in his eyes. I thought about what it must be like for him. Was he worried about our future? At only fifty years old, I was facing a life-threatening disease. My future would change, no matter what the outcome.

A nurse took some blood and a urine sample. I remember her coming back and saying with a chuckle, "Good news: Your pregnancy test came back negative!" That gave a bit of comic relief to my impending sense of doom. The nurse prepped me for surgery. I kissed Jim goodbye and away I went.

The lumpectomy with sentinel node biopsy went well. After several hours at the hospital, we returned home. I was a little sore and tired. They had put me in a special bra after the surgery that clipped in the front. I wore that bra for several days while I iced my breast and took Tylenol for pain. When it was time to wash the area, I carefully took the bra off and stared at myself in the mirror. It was all so surreal to me. There was an incision on the top of my right breast and one under my right armpit. I washed the areas, being very careful around the incision sites. I had difficulty getting the special bra back on and needed assistance from Jim.

I made sure before the surgery that I had shirts that buttoned down in the front. I was told by several of my friends who had gone through this surgery that it would not be easy to pull shirts over my head. Being prepared and asking questions ahead of time served me well.

November 13, 2017 - Post-Op Day #3

How do I feel?

Physically, I am less sore. The incision site under my arm burns a bit, and I feel sore where the tumor and some of my chest muscle were removed. I washed it and it feels better today.

Mentally, I feel better. I am wondering if I am a survivor. I am living at this very moment and survived my surgery, but I won't know the extent of my cancer until my post-op visit on November 21st, when I meet with the breast surgeon. Please, God, hoping she got clear margins, no lymph node involvement, and a low Oncotype DX Score.

Am I mad? No. Just thinking how ironic and unexpected that I was diagnosed with breast cancer. Was that why

I was interested in doing volunteer work for Komen for the past five years?

While doing my volunteer work, I often thought, 'What would I do if I was ever diagnosed with breast cancer?' I always thought there was no question I would get a double mastectomy. I was basing that thought on nothing. I didn't know much about this disease, but knew others who had gone through it and had a double mastectomy. Now that I was faced with the diagnosis and researched it, I listened to the doctors. A lumpectomy with sentinel node biopsy was the recommendation by both surgeons.

Going to Karmanos Cancer Institute and knowing my friend Laura, who worked there and helped with recommending a breast surgeon, was my saving grace. Were people like Laura put in my path for a reason? I felt like I was in the right place when I walked into Karmanos for the first time. Walking into a cancer institute was scary, but my fears were comforted by so many who worked there.

*The phone calls from my Komen family giving me encouragement and support make this journey so much more tolerable. Many put my mind at ease. If it were not for Komen and these people, I would have looked at my breast cancer diagnosis differently. I would have initially thought, 'I am going to die,' but **NOT SO**!*

Jim reminded me about all the survivors and the honor guard holding their signs during Opening Ceremonies when we attended the Komen Detroit Race for the

Cure. "Remember Jo," he said, "The five-year, the ten-year, the fifteen-year, the twenty-year, the twenty-five-year survivors... You will be one too."

I WILL BE A SURVIVOR!

I WILL GET THROUGH THIS!

I WILL GAIN STRENGTH!

Am I sad? YES. Sad that there is cancer and that it can happen to anyone. But happy for the support, the research, and the work I have already put forth to help fight this disease. As I reflect, I believe it was no coincidence that I began volunteering for Komen Detroit Race for the Cure. God has a plan for your life. God put Komen in my life to help me and keep me strong.

God, continue to heal me and get me to a good, positive place where maybe I can be the help I have received.

What is the lesson? I am not sure yet because the journey has just begun.

This journal entry brings me back to those days after my lumpectomy, sitting on my couch, recuperating and writing in my journal. Tears running down my face, thinking how sad this had happened to me—fearful of what would come in the following weeks. But then, a sense of inner strength came over me the more I thought about it. A voice deep inside whispered, *"You can do this. You will do this."* You go through so many emotions at each stage of this journey. Each is unique, and each is a lesson learned.

November 14, 2017

Is our destiny laid out for us? I believe yes, it is. God knew I would face this obstacle in my life, so He put things in divine order. To make it easier for me, He put particular people in my path. Yvette was put in my path to introduce me to Komen. She was then diagnosed with breast cancer herself. I was able to turn to her when I was diagnosed to ask questions and receive reassurance. Komen became a passion, and I didn't quite know why. I thought it was because we supported women like Yvette, and being an advocate was what I became while volunteering. But what was the more significant meaning for me? Being part of Komen gave me friendships and taught me about survivorship. Today I can say I am a survivor.

Cancer can happen to anyone. Cancer is part of my life now. Thank You, God, for putting Komen in my life, for without it, I would be in a much darker, lonelier place. Thank you, Mo, for telling me what I already knew, but hearing it again today rang so true and shook me. Me: "Mo, I don't have many risk factors for breast cancer." Mo: "You're a woman, and you are getting older." Those are the two most common risk factors to getting breast cancer. We are all at risk.

God knew and helped lessen this burden for me, I am now sure. Thank You, God, for making this easier and placing people in my life who can help me on this journey. Women who have experienced and endured this breast cancer before me have made it easier. I have been blessed and continue to be blessed by Your love and guidance, God.

Coincidence or not? I recall a woman who came up to me after Komen's September Celebration earlier this year, complimenting me on my speaking abilities. Is this the next step in my journey? Do others need to hear my story? Will it help? Is this my purpose? I think it is too early to tell, but I just wanted to jot it down right now as something to think about for my future.

As I reread this entry, I am taken aback by all that I wrote and the foreshadowing of my life, given this breast cancer diagnosis was not easy for me to fathom. At times, I felt frozen within my own body, but as I researched each step I was to go through, it gave me a sense of empowerment. I knew I would eventually get through doctor appointments, surgery, and treatments. If I could get through this, I knew others could too. That's when I began thinking maybe my voice could be a guide to help others diagnosed with breast cancer.

Chapter 7
A Surprising Turn Of Events

As I was skimming through a book one morning, I came across this poem. It moved me, so I decided it needed to be kept and written down in my journal.

November 20, 2017

Always Have Faith

Never give up. Never lose hope.
Always have faith, it allows you to cope.
Trying times will pass, as they always do.
Just have patience, your dreams will come true.
So put on a smile, you'll live through your pain.
Know it will pass, and strength you will gain.
                                    ~ Charlie Remiggio

I feel strong today. I just went out for a walk up and down the block. It is a bright, brisk, sunny day. It felt good.

Tomorrow, I find out my pathology report results. Please, God, let everything be good. I am hopeful the surgeon got clear margins and I have no lymph node involvement.

This has been the most fear I have felt in my entire life. It is frightening facing your mortality. It is something I never would have imagined. But, I am strong and positive. I have surrounded myself with great people who are cheering for me. Their positive energy and mine will get me through whatever I will face.

November 22, 2017

God is Good!

I cannot express the feeling that came over me when my breast surgeon came into the exam room and said, "I have good news; your biopsy report shows you have Invasive Ductal Carcinoma, Stage I." She went on to say she had gotten clear margins with no lymph node involvement. The best-case scenario!

I wanted to cry but kept my composure as I listened to her explain the next course of action. I will meet with an oncologist and discuss a treatment plan. The most probable path of treatment will be RADIATION and NO CHEMOTHERAPY.

After the appointment, as Jim and I reached the lobby, I cried. They were tears of joy, relief, and gratitude. I know I have a way to go, but this first hurdle is over.

December 15, 2017

*A surprising turn of events has unfolded in the past several weeks. My breast surgeon called to let me know there was a discrepancy between my original biopsy report and my final tumor pathology report. My original breast biopsy report stated that my tumor was Progesterone and Estrogen Positive AND **HER2- NEGATIVE**. The TUMOR they had removed from my breast came back with a pathology report stating that my tumor was Progesterone and Estrogen Positive AND **HER2-POSITIVE**. What??? How could this be?*

She explained to me that biopsy reports are not always conclusive. A hard-boiled egg analogy helped me understand. When placing a fine needle in a hard-boiled egg, they can go into an area where it is all white and miss the yellow yoke (the HER2 part), thus coming up with my biopsy report of HER2-negative. When they did the lumpectomy and removed the tumor, they tested it by taking slices to determine what type of cancer was present. When they did that in the lab, it tested triple positive (Progesterone, Estrogen, and HER2-positive). The actual tumor report was my definitive diagnosis. She explained that the course of treatment would now change drastically. Instead of only a month of radiation, I would first need chemotherapy and an antibody treatment to treat the HER2. I would then go on to radiation.

After my biopsy two months ago, one of my primary concerns was whether it tested HER2-positive, an aggressive type of cancer. One of my biggest fears had now come true.

I feverishly started research, and here is some information I found about HER2-positive breast cancer:

* HER2-positive breast cancer is breast cancer that tests positive for a protein called human epidermal growth factor receptor 2 (HER2). This protein promotes the growth of cancer cells.

* Approximately one in every five breast cancers, twenty percent, have cancer cells that have extra copies of the gene that makes the HER2 protein. HER2-positive breast

cancers tend to be more aggressive than other types of breast cancer.

✳ Treatments that specifically target HER2 are very effective. These treatments are so effective that the prognosis for HER2-positive breast cancer is quite good.

✳ Certain standard chemotherapy drugs can also effectively treat HER2-positive breast cancers, although these drugs don't specifically target the HER2 protein.

✳ Experts recommend that every invasive breast cancer be tested for the presence of HER2 because the results significantly impact treatment recommendations.[1]

Now, back to my journal entry...

I anxiously awaited the appointment with the oncologist after learning the new diagnosis. After meeting with the oncologist, a treatment plan was set before me. The longevity of treatment seems daunting. It will take approximately one year to get through my treatment, but here are the positives:

1. *The chemotherapy, which I will receive weekly for twelve weeks, is not as harsh of a chemo as other types. It has fewer side effects.*

2. *It is Stage I breast cancer, so the prognosis is excellent.*

3. *If I go through all the treatments explained to me, my five-year survival rate is ninety-seven percent.*

4. *One year of treatment is just a bump in the road of my life journey.*

5. *I am thankful they found the discrepancy, and now I will be receiving the correct treatment.*

I know this is difficult for Jim. I have been attacking him with my words. I have no other outlet. He has bore the brunt of my anger with this turn of events. Seeing all the tears in his eyes today after the oncologist appointment confirmed his love for me. I know he feels just awful. I must be more mindful of his feelings and the turmoil he must be experiencing.

Moving forward, I now have a plan, and I will need to take CANCER one day at a time. My strong FAITH in GOD and HOPE will get me through this rocky road. Now telling my mother the news today will be one of the most challenging things I will do. God give me the strength I need to say to her that I have breast cancer. I will convey, that with all the treatment, I will be fine. I wish I did not have to tell her any of this and cause her grief.

Looking back at all that had transpired indeed was astonishing and very unexpected. To realize a biopsy report could be inconclusive or somewhat wrong confused me. Up until now, I have said I was sad, not mad, but I have to say this change of my course in treatment got me pretty revved up and even more frightened about my future. If left untreated, the reality is this breast cancer would kill me.

Now I faced chemotherapy, side effects like losing my hair, and many other symptoms. I would look different. By looking at me, people would now know I was sick. When the original plan was to have a month of radiation only as my treatment, I thought I would not even have to burden my mother with the cancer diagnosis. My mother was ninety years old when I was diagnosed and suffered from her own health issues. I didn't want to add any more stress. However, now, because of all the potential side effects, I would need to tell her, which made me sad. No one ever wants to see their daughter go through cancer.

I went to visit my mother that same day. She was in her bedroom, resting. As I walked into her dimly-lit room, a big smile came over her face. She was happy to see me. We chatted about everyday things like the weather and what I was making for dinner. Then I said the words no mother wishes ever to hear:

"Mom, remember I told you I had a mammogram? I had a biopsy and received the results, which show I have breast cancer."

My mother's eyes grew big and her mouth dropped. The sadness I saw in her eyes broke my heart. After we talked about it at length, I am happy to say she took the news surprisingly well. My mother was one tough cookie who was a pillar of strength.

As I began my chemo treatments, I was well enough to visit my mother twice a week. It gave me great solace seeing her. You always need your mother, no matter how old you are and especially going through an illness like cancer. One day she asked if she could go to the chemo treatments. Unfortunately, my mother was wheelchair-bound and it would be difficult for her to come along, but the fact that she wanted to be by my side meant the world to me. I opened up to my mom that day, but it took longer for me to tell other family and friends about my diagnosis. I needed to let it set in with me.

I knew I had a great support system within Komen, so I turned to several of those I knew there first to listen to what they had gone through during treatment. It made me feel better hearing from these survivors. Their experiences made what I was about to embark on a little less scary. I had serious, meaningful conversations connecting with these great people on a level we had never discussed before, and that was a great comfort. There was Katrina, who'd had breast cancer eleven years before me. Her breast cancer was similar to mine. She was able to share her experience with the treatments. There was Carrie, who took me out to dinner one evening. Her mother was a survivor, and she knew how important support was to the cancer patient. She gave me a gift, a "Dammit Doll". Now, for those of you who have never heard of one, a Dammit Doll is a small stuffed doll that you can bang on things to get out your frustrations while saying, "dammit". It came in very handy on days when the side effects from chemo kicked in.

I can't say enough how important it is to have support going through such a terrifying time. I recall telling my dearest friend Carla about my diagnosis. We have been friends since childhood and shared so much of our lives' trials and tribulations. Initially, she was shocked when I told her the news. You do not expect your friend, whom you have known for forty-five years, to be diagnosed with cancer. She told me she didn't quite know how to handle it, but being the wonderful friend she is, she showed me so much support and listened to my many phone calls of aggravation.

I recall one particular evening when she came over to watch TV. It was Super Bowl Sunday. I was in chemotherapy at the time and I had very little hair left on my head. I felt comfortable around her not wearing my wig. We laughed, talked, and had such a great evening together. These beautiful acts of kindness filled me with such love. It made the day-to-day much more bearable.

Some people did not know what to say or do. At first, I was upset by this, but later I realized that certain people are not capable of going through something so sad and different to them.

I am embarrassed to say that one friend offered food, along with sitting at the hospital with my husband during my lumpectomy. These were things I did not need at the time. Later, I lashed out at her, saying she was not doing anything, which could not be further from the truth. I remember pleading, "Do something!" I felt lost and cried out for help.

As a cancer patient, if someone does not know what to say or do and they tell you so, *tell them your needs*. Let them know what that is, whether to lend an ear or come over for coffee and conversation. Remember, it is a trying time for your friends and loved ones too. Sharing this time will make a lasting impression.

CHAPTER 8
PREPARING FOR TREATMENT

As the preparation for treatment began, anxiety set in. I needed a minor outpatient procedure to have a port placed under my skin on the left upper side of my chest. The port is where you receive the chemotherapy and antibody treatments. I was to receive my first MUGA scan, a test that would measure the strength of my heart. One of the drugs I would be receiving can affect your heart, so they needed to monitor my heart function closely. All of it was very new to me. As each step of the treatment was presented to me, I continued my research to understand it better. I was a Physician Assistant, but we didn't learn the specifics of all the different types of breast cancers and the processes needed to get through them.

I was facing twelve rounds of chemotherapy, an antibody treatment called Herceptin, twenty rounds of radiation, then at least five years of an oral medication called Tamoxifen. It was quite a long journey.

Previous to being diagnosed, I had medium-length, dark brown (dyed) hair. My hair stylist suggested I get my hair cut short before beginning my chemo treatments, as one of her other clients had done, and it made the process of losing it a bit easier. My hair stylist and friend, Lisa, was terrific. She came to my home on a Sunday to cut my hair, as she knew it would be emotional for me and thought the salon was not the place to do it. Many empathetic souls were put in my life to help, and Lisa was one of them.

Sporting my new short haircut, my sister, Anna, and I went to a wig boutique recommended to me by a friend. The woman who helped me there was amazing. She picked out a wig that matched my current short hairstyle almost exactly, so no one would realize it was not my natural hair. When I was ready to shave my hair off, she told me to give her a call and she would do it in a private room at the boutique. She would then show me how to wear the wig. She also went through how to care for the wig. Who knew you needed special shampoo, conditioner, styling products, and a stand to dry it on! It was a relief to get this done. I felt in control and proactive by getting a wig. I was fortunate that my health insurance covered a portion of it. Another lesson learned: Wigs have a wide price range. Make sure to price them out and check with your insurance. If covered, get a prescription from your oncologist before ordering your wig.

When you go for chemo treatments, some days are long. I wondered, *'What do I bring?'* I asked several people who had gone through treatment for suggestions. In my "chemo day bag", I packed my Karmanos folder, holding all the business cards of my doctors, appointments, and test reports. I also packed a warm blanket. The rooms you receive your treatments in can be cool, so a warm blanket is comforting. I received several blankets as gifts after being diagnosed. People were so generous, and each time I covered up with one of the blankets, it would remind me of that particular person who had gifted it to me.

One specific blanket was incredibly soft with a red-and-black checkered pattern. My mother's caregiver, Gina, who had become a friend, gave it to me. Initially, when I was diagnosed and learned the extent of my treatment, I was so worried about how I would be able to help care for my mother. Gina assured me not to worry, that she would care for my mother. She told me to concentrate on my treatment, which gave me such relief.

I thought about the twelve rounds of chemo and how the oncologist had told me I would need a driver because of the drowsiness I would encounter due to the medications. Who would be able to take me? So many people I knew worked. Immediately, I thought of my husband. I asked him if he could use twelve of his vacation days to take me to my treatments. He was hesitant at first. He responded frankly, "Taking one day off would cut my work week by twenty percent." It was a very mechanical response to a crucial question. He explained that because of his job's amount of work and demands, he was concerned he could potentially fall behind with his work schedule. He suggested hiring someone to drive me. He looked into it and knew someone who recommended a driver.

To say I was astounded would be an understatement. My spouse, who I leaned on for support, considered not being by my side during my treatments. I was angry and hurt. What was that we'd said in our wedding vows? "In sickness and in health." Well, here was a big test, and unfortunately, he was failing miserably. A cancer diagnosis was one of the biggest obstacles we had encountered thus far in our life together. I could potentially die. Why would my spouse not want to stand by me? I understood his job was vital, he was our sole source of financial support at that time, but knowing he had more than enough vacation days and not wanting to use them was unsettling and heartbreaking.

We had many conversations up until the day of my first chemotherapy treatment. I was petrified, and the one thing he could do to ease my mind, by driving me, he would not do. Finally, one day I said, "If this was you and you needed a driver and someone by your side during your treatments, who would you choose?" He looked at me sheepishly and said, "You." I explained I did not want anyone but him to see me in such a vulnerable state. After that conversation, he understood. By putting things in perspective, he finally put my mind at ease by agreeing to be my driver.

Jim accompanied me to eleven of my twelve chemo treatments. He sat in the cubicle with me once a week as I received my treatments. I often wondered what was going through his mind, but never asked. Later, we had discussions about his thoughts and the fear of him losing me. Initially, he was in denial. It did not sink in for him until that first day of my treatment that his wife was now a cancer patient.

If you are married, spousal support is vital. You share a life with this person. This person is your best friend and the love of your life. Try to be the supportive spouse. Having that spouse walk alongside you during this journey can make a difference in your recovery.

CHAPTER 9
FIRST DAY OF CHEMOTHERAPY

With much trepidation, the first day of chemotherapy came. I had slept only a few hours. Jim and I awoke at five a.m. I showered and had a light breakfast. Before leaving, I was instructed to put lidocaine cream over the skin where my port was placed. The cream would numb the area and cause minimal discomfort when they accessed it with the needle. It was an hour car ride to the cancer institute. We left at six a.m.

Many things were running through my mind on that drive. Was I going to tolerate the chemo? How would I feel afterward? Why was this all happening to me? Jim dropped me off at the door and I went in. I have to say entering a cancer institute for my first chemotherapy treatment was overwhelming.

Everyone from the receptionists to the phlebotomists to the nurses were marvelous. I was taken back to my cubicle, which had three walls and an open front that you could draw a curtain for privacy. There was a seat for Jim to sit in, and I had a comfy recliner where I sat, waiting for the nurse. You get to know the nurses going through your weekly treatments. The infusion nurses were exceptional human beings, and each one put me at ease in their unique way. Once the nurse received my treatments and medications, she would come over and administer the meds needed. I was given Benadryl and steroids to help counter any allergic reactions. I was told the first infusion would go slow because they wanted to be very careful to monitor anything that might happen, such as allergic reactions.

It was a long first treatment day, lasting six hours. As they started the infusion of the chemotherapy drug, Taxol, I put my earbuds in and listened to some soothing music. My favorite to listen to was Enya. I drifted in and out of sleep. I slept most of the way home and lay on the couch the rest of the day. I hardly ate, but I remember reading I should stay hydrated. I drank eight glasses of water daily. By the evening, the steroids began to take effect so that I had a tremendous amount of energy. I started organizing my kitchen drawers and closets. See, there are silver linings to medication side effects too! But the steroids affected my sleep. I could hardly sleep, so I continued organizing and cleaning. The effects of the steroids wore off in about twenty-four hours and I calmed down.

I made sure every day I would walk. It was winter, so I walked laps in my basement listening to music. I had my favorites like Whitney Houston. Being a girl growing up in the 70's and 80's, I enjoyed pop music too. I would walk for thirty minutes. It was my goal to walk every day through treatment. I am happy to say I achieved that goal.

CHAPTER 10
HAIR LOSS

There were many side effects of chemotherapy; each conjured up different emotions. One of the worst side effects I encountered was the hair loss. It was most devastating. As I reflect on this loss, I realize as women, we wear our hair proudly; like a crown, it adorns our head. It is part of our identity. It shows others our personality and style. Without it, how would I be identified? It was frightening knowing this chemotherapy flowing through me, which could potentially save me, was causing such havoc with my body and life.

Losing my hair changed my outward appearance, but it was also changing me on the inside. I felt as if I was unraveling. It was overpowering. Unfortunately, hair loss showed the world I was sick. I didn't like that feeling of vulnerability. Was it really about the physical loss of my hair that I disliked or the loss of control? I would have to say the latter. Not controlling what was physically happening to me made me crazy at times. Some days, it seemed like I was living in a horror movie. How would it end? It was a scary, lonely place that I wish no one had to be in and experience.

After much reflection, I realized that going through all of this was shaping the new me. A year later, after treatment, I realized my hair did not define me. What defined me was so much more, and the transformation inside me was impressive. I was stronger. I could look fear in the face and know I could conquer anything that came my way after living through my breast cancer journey.

January 25, 2018

I feel like I am in a terrible dream. I started losing my hair today. I had dreaded and anticipated this day. It is day 16 of chemotherapy treatment. The oncologist said I would begin losing my hair around day 17. I hope it stays like this, a gradual hair loss. I don't know if I can handle the clumps they say might come out. My scalp is itchy and has dry patches. Tomorrow is my third chemo treatment. I am uneasy tonight. Last week did not go so great. They had difficulty accessing my port, then I had shortness of breath, which was an allergic reaction. My hope is everything goes smoothly tomorrow.

I was so grateful for a beautiful diversion from this initial hair loss. My friend Eileen and I planned a field trip to the Monet Exhibit at the Detroit Institute of Arts. After seeing the exhibit, we went to lunch and stopped at Avalon International Breads to buy some treats. We ended the day by walking into Flo's, next to the bakery, for some hat shopping!! I love my new hat and it was such a fun day. I am grateful for the beautiful friendship I have formed with Eileen.

January 26, 2018

Third chemo/Herceptin treatment today. This morning I was fearful. I was shedding hair, a lot of hair. I could not believe all the hair in the sink, on the bathroom floor, on my clothes, and stuck to my neck and chest.

January 30, 2018

I lost more hair today. I washed my hair and it was everywhere—in the drain, on the floor, in the sink, on the toilet—EVERYWHERE! I blow-dried it and hair flew all around me. It even stuck to the bathroom walls. It is very emotional. You would not know I was getting chemo if you looked at me. Once my hair is gone, I will know. It becomes even more real. I am petrified. I am worried how I will look once I lose all my hair. How long will it take for my hair to grow back? What will it look like? How will all of this change me? This seems like it isn't happening to me, but it is.

I cannot continue watching my hair fall out much longer. Today, I called the woman who sold me the wig. She said she would shave my hair off, then show me how to put the wig on. Will I look pretty? Will people know it's a wig? How will it make me feel? I know it will grow back. I know I will survive this part of the journey. It is just SO HARD.

January 31, 2018

I am pretty sure I will get my hair shaved off today. My head was so itchy last night. I am still very apprehensive. I don't know how I will feel after it happens. Some people say it is liberating. I hope so.

January 31, 2018 (Second Entry)

I must embrace this hair loss. It is part of the process. I made it to almost three weeks of treatment before losing my hair. Nine weeks to go of treatment, then the hair starts growing back. That is the positive.

God is good. If He put me in it, He will get me through it. AMEN. God is within me. God, give me the strength to get through today and come out okay with my hair being gone. *Your love is unwavering. I love You and know You will get me through this ordeal.*

I feel my dad with me today. I could hear him say, "Everything will be okay, Jo." I feel his presence. He is with me, his hand on my shoulder.

January 31, 2018 (Third Entry)

I got my hair buzzed off! The woman at the boutique was just incredible. She made the process so much easier. I thought I would be more emotional, but I was good with it. At first, I was unsure, but I even looked into the mirror as she shaved my head. Jim came for support and that was helpful too. He made me feel at ease, telling me how good I looked, and you know what? I do! I was happy to see that my bald head had a nice shape, and the little stubble of gray and black left gave me character.

I look like Sinead O'Conner, the Irish singer. The wig looks good on me too. She took the time to restyle it and showed me how to put it on for myself. At her suggestion, Jim and I went out to dinner.

Before getting my hair buzzed, I thought there was no way I was going out after the experience. But after I saw how natural the wig looked, I thought, 'I can do this! Let's go out and sort of celebrate.' They say shaving your hair off is liberating. I guess, in a way, it is. I know I felt a lot of relief. I had felt so nervous about losing my hair, up until the point of getting it shaved off. Afterward, I felt lighter. I felt free, as if some weight was lifted from my shoulders. Mentally, I think I will be okay.

On the heels of this momentous day, good news came to us. My niece and goddaughter, Laura, who is pregnant, learned she is having a baby girl! What a blessing! I feel her due date, June 23, my birthday, has a special meaning. This baby is going to give me HOPE. I HOPE the future holds wonderful things for the both of us. I cannot wait to meet her.

As I look back on this day, I notice I wrote three separate entries in my journal. You can imagine the multitude of emotions I underwent. The silver lining to the last entry was the fantastic news about a beautiful, great-niece to be born. You have to remind yourself that life does continue around you during treatment. It is nice to take in every bit of the good and that little niece being born was a special event to embrace.

Unfortunately, the hair loss overpowered so much of what was going on at the time in my life. Seeing my hair falling out was not easy. One day anger engulfed me and I started pulling hair out of my head. I screamed, "LOOK AT THIS!" to Jim and threw the large clumps of hair on the floor. It was one of the most disturbing parts of my cancer journey.

As I said in the journal entry, it was a relief to get my hair shaved off. Some people shave their hair off before their chemo treatment even starts. I guess for me, in some way, I thought maybe it wouldn't be so bad, so I waited to see how bad it would get before deciding to shave it off.

I was surprised that my hair started falling out almost to the day the oncologist said I should expect it would. You not only lose hair from your head, but everywhere it grows on your body. The only positive is that I did not have to shave under my arms or legs for several months.

Although this was difficult, it was not the only side effect I encountered. I had loose bowel movements throughout treatment. I began getting a metallic taste in my mouth, so food did not taste good, but I maintained my appetite. I would joke and say, "Leave it to me, a cancer patient who cannot even lose weight!" To my surprise, I never vomited and rarely was nauseous. I had a parched mouth and constantly drank water. My nose was dry and had clotted blood coming out of it at night. Unfortunately, the steroids made me very cranky, which was a huge downfall for those around me. About three days after chemo day, I would begin to feel better.

As chemotherapy continued, I experienced peripheral neuropathy (numbness and tingling of the hands and feet). After the treatment, some of the neuropathy reversed, but some was left in my toes. There are so many different chemotherapies used for cancer treatment, and the side effects differ from person to person. This is a glimpse into the window of what I experienced.

As my hair loss continued, I worried about my mom having to see me lose my hair. My wig looked so close to my natural hairstyle that I decided not to tell her that I would lose my hair. My father had gone through chemotherapy, and the type he received did not have any hair-loss side effects. I did not want to put any excess worry on my mother, so why tell her. I wore my wig each time I saw her while going through treatment. She never realized it was a wig; it looked that good! As chemotherapy continued, the steroids made my face more rounded, and at times, I would get flushed. My mother would comment on those things, and I explained it was the side effects to the medication. Once chemotherapy finished, my hair began to grow back. Initially, it came back a bit wavy, which was a welcome change because my hair had been poker straight all my life. The color was salt and pepper as it grew in.

I continued to wear the wig each time I visited my mother, but the summer months were upon us, and that wig was getting hot to wear. I have to chuckle now as I think about keeping the wig in the backseat of my car just in case I would stop by to visit my mom. I would put it on while in the car in her driveway. How would I explain the color change and style to my mom once I stop showing up wearing this wig? One hot June day, I had my wig on and went for a visit. I told my mom I was thinking about cutting my hair very short and letting it go gray. My mom's eyes grew big, and she said she thought I would never do such a thing.

I entered her home with no wig and sporting my very short hair the next day. My mother was so surprised and said, "Josephine, what did you do?!" We laughed after her initial shock, and I answered, "I told you I would cut my hair and go gray, Mom." As I sat next to my mother in her living room that day, she looked at me, and after a while, she smiled and said that I looked pretty and she honestly liked my new hairstyle. What a cherished, sweet moment between us. No harm done telling a little "white" lie to save my dear mother from heartache.

February 2, 2018

Today is treatment number four. I am a little uneasy this morning, but physically, I feel good. I meditated, relaxed, and walked for thirty minutes. I AM STRONG! I CAN DO THIS! After today, eight more treatments. NO

ONE WILL LET ME FEEL LESS THAN WHO I KNOW I AM! I surround myself with kind, loving people and positive energy.

February 2, 2018 (Second Entry)

I made it back from chemo and the oncology appointment. They were both good visits. They were able to access my port with no problems today. The oncologist said I was doing well. The nurse practitioner answered all my questions about my side effects. The fatigue and the loose stool were common. She did tell me, that around the seventh treatment, I will begin to experience neuropathy in my feet. She said they will monitor it, and sometimes after chemotherapy treatment has ended, the neuropathy is reversed.

I got into chemo early and was done by 12:30! The nurse said my infusions should be 2-2½ hours now. The Benadryl knocked me out and I slept the entire ride home.

I AM STRONG! I AM BEAUTIFUL! I AM A FIGHTER!

Eileen and me sporting our new hats.

Me after getting my hair shaved off.

CHAPTER 11
SEX AND INTIMACY

Early in my breast cancer journey, my oncologist discussed what would happen to me as I began chemotherapy treatments. I was fifty years old and still having my monthly cycle. He explained that the chemotherapy would push me into menopause. He called it chemo-induced menopause. Now, imagine going through the side effects of treatment along with experiencing menopause symptoms. It was not a pretty combination of hot flashes, night sweats, mood swings, fatigue, hair loss, and vaginal dryness.

A topic not talked much about during this cancer journey is sex and intimacy. To be honest, sex was the furthest thing from my mind during this time of my life. At this point, I'd had the lumpectomy, which still left my right breast sensitive. I did not want to have my right breast touched. I would refer to it as my "sick" breast. I had a port on the left side of my upper chest. All of it was not an attractive sight. Looking like this made sexual intimacy challenging. I did not feel pretty at all.

In October 2021, four years after my initial diagnosis, I was invited to be a guest speaker on a podcast talking about breast cancer. During the podcast, I was asked how I handled intimacy during treatment. The question surprised me. I had never been asked about this topic. A man had asked this question, and he wanted to know about it as his partner had had a double mastectomy and was going through breast cancer treatments. I could not talk about the double mastectomy part because I'd had a lumpectomy.

I paused as I thought about how to answer this sensitive question. I replied by saying, "There are many ways other than sex to be intimate. Hugging, holding hands, kissing, and caressing are good ways to start. Using endearing words, telling your partner you love them, and sharing all the unique qualities you admire about them is all part of intimacy." I felt it was a time when you could enhance your relationship by connecting with your partner on a different level.

Having a frank discussion with your partner, discussing that there should be no sexual expectations, is a good idea on days when you know it is not something you are interested in doing. It is important to discuss sex and the ability or inability to have it with your partner. Talking openly to each other may relieve tension and worry. Remember, your partner may be fearful as well. Talking honestly about what kinds of activities may cause sensitivity can help you relax. Explaining to your partner that vaginal dryness can make sex painful and uncomfortable may help them understand. Your partner needs to know what you are experiencing. Each of us goes through different symptoms. A conversation between your oncologist, you, and your partner may be helpful.

For me, sex was difficult, but with the help of some vaginal creams and lubricants recommended by my nurse practitioner, it made it tolerable. It was not a focus as I was going through treatment. My focus was on the treatments and getting better so I could return to a healthy sex life one day.

CHAPTER 12
LESSONS LEARNED

Cancer changes you as a person. Every experience you go through in life teaches you something you didn't know. Many lessons are learned along the way. You encounter so many remarkable people through your journey. I learned that these people affect you and your destiny.

February 10, 2018

I had my fifth treatment yesterday. Everything went smoothly. I had a nurse who accessed my port with no issues. I had an infusion nurse who was magnificent too. She answered all my questions and gave me a lotion recommendation for my foot neuropathy. Another nurse took the needle out from my port with no pain. We had a short conversation and realized we shared the same birthday. It was a blessing to be surrounded by such sincere people during such a difficult time.

Jim and I sat in the lobby waiting for the valet to bring our car as I left treatment. A woman was sitting across from me. She looked so sickly, from her skin tone to the expression on her face. I could tell she was with her sister and there also were two children. A boy who appeared to be about eight years old was sitting alongside this sickly woman. She was very patient with him, explaining he needed to sit still while they waited for their car. She then looked at me and said, "I spoiled him; I didn't know I would get cancer. I will be all right." I just smiled; then she got up and left.

The woman sitting next to me said, "God bless her." My eyes welled up with tears. Sadness engulfed me. Here was a woman who appeared very ill, yet she wanted me to know she would be all right for her son. I saw a strength in her that I only hope I will possess. It is hard to see how this affects your family, children, and friends.

At times, I feel so surrounded by love, and at other times I feel so alone.

God help me. I must never forget God is with me. I can feel my father with me today. He is my guardian angel.

February 17, 2018

Yesterday I had my sixth chemo treatment. I am halfway done! It went smoothly, but my oncologist thinks my port tubing may be infected. He said to watch it closely. If the redness worsens or I get a temperature, he said to go to the Emergency Room. The Physician Assistant in Interventional Radiology looked at it today and said it is not so bad and prescribed Keflex, an antibiotic. She said they could do a study where they inject dye into the port to see if there is leaking from the tube. If it is leaking, it will need to come out. I need a prescription for the procedure. She scheduled the procedure for Tuesday. I see the Oncology Nurse Practitioner on Tuesday to see how my skin looks around the port. I will tell her I want the study done regardless and get the script from her. I asked Karen to come with me to be a second set of ears and to be a driver if I needed the port to come out. I am grateful my sister-in-law will do this for me. I want to remain positive. I know the antibiotics will help this improve.

February 21, 2018

I met with the Nurse Practitioner and she gave me the prescription to have the procedure to check my port tubing. I had the procedure and all went well. Nothing was wrong with the tubing and no leaking was present. I did not need to have it taken out. I was relieved.

February 23, 2018

Treatment number seven of twelve today. Once I get through today, I feel I will be climbing down the other side of this chemo mountain. Please, God, give me the strength I need to get this done.

Stay Positive. Do not let negativity enter this day.

YOU ARE STRONG.
YOU ARE BEAUTIFUL.
YOU CAN GET THROUGH THIS.

February 25, 2018

Treatment number seven is done. I met with the oncologist, and he said I am doing well, but the neuropathy I am experiencing may worsen and stay. The side effects have been tolerable, and for that, I am grateful. I keep doing my best. I exercise every day, meditate, pray, read, and write in this journal. It is all helping.

March 2, 2018

I fell asleep early at 7:00 p.m. and now I am wide awake at 1:00 a.m.

Today is my eighth treatment. I hope all goes well. I feel that once this one is over, I will feel more relief. I will be two-thirds through with the Taxol/Herceptin treatment.

I had a skin reaction on my face and neck. I am not sure why this happened.

God, give me the strength to endure the rest of my treatment. I know You are always with me.

March 3, 2018

I got through treatment eight of twelve!

It was tough accessing my port today, but the nurse's perseverance got me through it, and after she administered the "clot buster", it worked!

The nurse made me feel so at ease. I slept through most of the treatment.

I need to hydrate and watch my diet this week. My weight is creeping up. YIKES!

March 10, 2018

I was very anxious going into my ninth treatment today. I have suffered some severe side effects this past week. The neuropathy in my feet and fingertips has gotten worse. One night the numbness in my feet turned to pain. I fear this neuropathy will not reverse, but I must try to remain positive.

I met with the nurse practitioner today, and she decided to hold the Taxol but administer the Herceptin. We will reevaluate everything next week. She said if the neuropathy symptoms lessen, they may move forward next week with Taxol, but at a dosage reduction of twenty-five percent.

My hands are also very red on the tops, and she said it is a side effect of the Taxol. Redness wrapped around my lower thumb and went around to the first digit. I hope the neuropathy lessens and this redness on my hands goes away.

I was thrilled the nurse accessed my port with no problems!

The day was a good one. I was happy the nurse practitioner decided to hold the Taxol. I need a break. Three more treatments!

I was also so happy to see Katrina with Laura today. They came looking for me. Katrina remembered I had told her I would be at Karmanos on Friday, so she came early before her meeting to see me. It was so lovely and a much-needed surprise. I am constantly thankful to my Komen family.

On reflection and after speaking with the nurse practitioner today, I believe there is a much bigger purpose for me and the lessons learned by getting this breast cancer diagnosis. I have been involved with Komen for five years, and even though I worked to raise money and be part of the Race, I never really truly understood the whole picture of the breast cancer patient. Now, I do. I believe I was put on this path to be an advocate and to teach others about breast cancer. This has been God's plan for me.

BE STRONG!
YOU GOT THIS, GIRL!

As I reread these last entries, I am amazed at all I thought and endured. I was reminded of the tough times I had gone through with the side effects. I remember my hands being so red; it felt like a bad sunburn. The neuropathy had gotten so bad it felt like I was walking through wet cement. One morning I caught a glimpse of myself in the mirror. I had to take a second look. I did not recognize the person staring back at me. At that point of treatment, I had lost all the hair on my head. My face was puffy because of the steroids. Who was I? What had happened to me? It was a sad moment, but I always maintained hope and had the bigger picture of my future in my mind. The thought that I was nearing the end of treatment excited me. It was reaching a goal I never wished I had to attain.

March 16, 2018

I am going to meet with the oncologist. Today, I am nervous. Will he continue Taxol? I know it was good to break from it, but I can't help thinking, will it cause any setbacks because I missed a dose? What about this awful rash on my hands? I have three more treatments to go. I just want to get through the next three weeks and have this part of the treatment done. My oncologist is very knowledgeable. He will have the answers and know how to proceed. I must trust him and know he will put my best interests first.

GIRL, YOU KNOW YOU ARE ALMOST THERE.
JUST BREATHE.

March 23, 2018 (Morning Entry)

Today I can see the finish line, the first part of my treatment being over. Chemo is almost done. I have two more treatments. After today, I will have just one more; then I will rejoice at Easter.

Easter—a new beginning for me.

I will begin the next phase of treatment.

KEEP GOING, GIRL.
YOU GOT THIS.
YOU ARE SURROUNDED BY LOVE AND SUPPORT.

March 23, 2018 (Evening Entry)

Today was my eleventh treatment.

I met with my oncologist, and we mutually decided to add in the Taxol this week after a two-week break. He seems to think the rash outbreak on my hands was an accumulation of Taxol in my body.

He talked a bit about radiation, and I am waiting to hear from Karmanos for a Radiation Oncology appointment. He said I would probably start two-to-four weeks after chemo is done. I will need a MUGA scan soon to check on my heart. They need to monitor my heart function because of the Herceptin infusions.

We discussed I would start Tamoxifen shortly after chemo. I told him I had reservations about Tamoxifen. He said the side effects are less than what you go through with chemo. I told him it was more about the length of time involved with taking Tamoxifen that was concerning. I would be on it anywhere from five-to-ten years. I told him I could do just about anything for three months, meaning the chemo.

Some of the things I have read about in my private cancer Facebook groups about Tamoxifen and the side effects, including weight gain, night sweats, fluid retention, fatigue, and nausea, was troubling to me. The rare severe problems of deep vein thrombosis (DVT), stroke, and uterine cancer were concerning. My oncologist reassured me that Tamoxifen is a potentially lifesaving drug. It has been revolutionary in the treatment of breast cancer. It is an effective hormone therapy used to treat hormone receptor-positive breast cancer, including my diagnosis. It can significantly reduce the risk of cancer recurrence. My thoughts now are to research it more. I guess I did not realize I would be going on it so soon. All this information is so overwhelming.

During my infusion today, I experienced something remarkable. After beginning my chemo infusion, I heard a beautiful voice singing. I was not sure if it was coming from the piped-in radio music or a real person. I asked my nurse, "Is someone singing?" She said, "Yes, the woman in the cubicle next to you." It was so beautiful, and I wish I could remember the words because she kept repeating them. It was religious. She was singing of God and strength. I got up to go to the bathroom, and on my way back, I wanted to thank her and tell her how I enjoyed her voice, but as I peeked into the cubicle next to me, it was empty. I questioned, "Was she an angel?"

We ended the day taking a ride in Jim's new Challenger and went for coffee in Lake Orion. We listened to a young woman playing the guitar and enjoyed a pleasant conversation together.

Thank you, God, for a good day. One more chemo treatment to go!

I remember the conversation with my oncologist that day. I was excited that I was almost done with chemo, but my infusions of Herceptin would continue. Knowing I was going onto radiation seemed, at that time, almost a relief, but I soon learned radiation has its own set of hurdles.

The beautiful singing coming from the cubicle next to me was magical. It was so encouraging to hear such uplifting words. At that moment, I realized how other people coped, and it made me feel better, giving me a glimpse into another cancer patient's journey. It indeed was a good day. Chemotherapy does have its lessons and silver linings.

Chapter 13
Co-Survivors and A Husband's Perspective

Up until now, I have talked about MY journey, but cancer doesn't affect just you; it affects those around you and those you love. Those people who walk alongside you on your journey are called co-survivors. Support is needed well beyond treatment into survivorship. These supporters include your spouse, parents, siblings, coworkers, and friends.

It is a very emotional time and many relationships are tested. A cancer diagnosis can devastate relationships, but it also can enhance them. My cancer diagnosis brought my sister Anna and me closer together. She was so kind to me, cooked for me once a week, and told me she prayed for me daily. My cousin Linda, who lives in Montreal, would send me a message every Friday morning before I had treatment. I looked forward to her motivational message each week.

My friend Delaney, a young cancer survivor, knew just what I needed. I received motivational cards and gifts from her when I least expected them, and her timing was impeccable. My friend Marybeth lived in Pennsylvania and was another of my co-survivors. Though we were miles apart, we bonded over having health issues coinciding. Those nights I could not sleep, I would message her, and sure enough, she would be awake. We would talk about our feelings and all that was going on in our lives. It was a comfort knowing someone like Marybeth was there for me in the dark quietness of the night when my mind wandered wildly.

Today in my survivorship, I have an exceptional friend, Sherry, who is encouraging and positive. She supported my dreams of writing this book. She sends motivational cards, texts, and gifts. She talks to me whenever I need someone to listen to my frustrations and triumphs.

I appreciate all the support from so many people in my life. I recall all of these people who traveled with me, some I mentioned earlier in this book. I could go on and on, and forgive me if I do not mention you all. What you did for me did not go unnoticed. These people helped me immensely and made the journey more tolerable. Be that co-survivor to someone you know who is going through cancer. Be by their side. It is an important role to fill and will mean so much to both involved.

Through this journey, I would have to say the person who walked alongside me daily and witnessed what I encountered both physically and mentally was my husband Jim. At times it was difficult to see him tolerate what I was experiencing. I never would have imagined our marriage vows would be challenged at such a young age. We were both fifty years old at my diagnosis and married twenty-five years. It tested our relationship and our love. I was angry at times and he was as well; we got into some heated arguments. Certain days I felt helpless and wanted him to be my rock. That's a lot for a spouse to handle. I look back now and realize we were both far from perfect. Going through everything ultimately made our marriage stronger.

I asked Jim if he could share some of his thoughts and what he went through as my husband and co-survivor. Here are some of his words of wisdom.

"It was a tough time for me when Josephine was diagnosed with cancer. I didn't quite know what to do or say to her. I was

in denial and often tried to avoid talking about her cancer. The seriousness of her diagnosis was at the forefront of my mind, and I wanted to help but didn't know what she needed. In retrospect, I wish I had attended a cancer support group or researched the role of a co-survivor. It would have made things a lot easier for both of us.

"Later, and after Josephine's treatment, I learned there were three primary types of support: informational, practical, and emotional.[2] I was more focused on informational and practical support as I looked back. I didn't understand the emotional toll Josephine's cancer had on her. At times, she would become sad, angry, or frustrated, and I would retreat because I was at a loss for what to do. The type and amount of support may differ depending on the person a co-survivor is supporting and their stage at their particular part of their journey. I want to share some information on the types of support.

"Informational support is learning about the specifics of the diagnosis and treatment and asking questions at appointments. Josephine has a medical background and understands the science. I couldn't provide much additional help with that part because my experience was not medical. She would make a list of questions before each of her appointments. I was able to help by taking notes as Josephine asked questions. I would make sure she didn't forget to ask anything she had on her list. Afterward, we would compare notes and discuss what we'd heard. I believe this helped me as much as it helped her. It made me address her cancer head-on. We were in this together. Initially, I would leave many of the appointments confused. As time went on and I learned more, it was easier to understand Josephine's

diagnosis and how the disease, treatment, and medication affected her. It also helped me to provide practical support.

"Practical support is doing things, big or small, for your loved one. Some practical support I provided was cleaning the house, bringing her a warm cup of tea, and picking up her prescriptions. By doing these things, I was showing Josephine I cared about her.

"As I mentioned, where I struggled was how to provide emotional support. Josephine will be the first to say I wasn't born with a strong empathy gene. I jokingly tell her that she has enough empathy for both of us. But this was different. It wasn't about not caring. It was about my lack of understanding of the disease and my fear of losing her. When I first started driving Josephine to appointments, I saw this as something anyone could do if I had a work conflict. We tried another driver early on, and it added more stress. Would her driver be late? What if there was a last-minute conflict? I didn't realize Josephine was asking me to do this not because I'm a good driver (I'm not, I drive too fast), but because she was afraid. She wanted me with her as she worked through the maze of doctors and facilities for her treatment. It was also about me being there when she got her chemo treatment to talk to her and hold her hand. This became clear to me after I attended the chemo treatments and saw the effect on her body. I was mistaking her request for emotional support for practical support.

"Josephine is through the first part of her journey and is now in survivorship. The role of a co-survivor doesn't end here. There are medications, follow-up appointments, and frequent mammograms. Those mammogram appointments are scary for Josephine and trigger memories of her initial diagnosis. I have made it a priority to attend these and be there for emotional support.

"What would I do better or recommend to other co-survivors? First, do some research. Try to understand the entire journey, treatment options, and possible outcomes. You may want to consider a co-survivor support group if you have a hard time with your role. Also, if you are unsure what to do, just ask, 'What can I do to help?' or 'Is there anything I can get for you to make you more comfortable?' At times, I find it best to just listen to Josephine when she is upset. I have learned you don't always need to solve the problem or give an opinion. At times I would say, 'Everything will be all right,' but sometimes that is not true. Saying, 'I'll be there for you no matter what,' can be reassuring. And most importantly, say, 'I love you.'

"I hope my shared perspective helps co-survivors supporting a loved one through their cancer journey."

CHAPTER 14
CELEBRATION!

March 29, 2018

My last chemo treatment is tomorrow! I am excited, happy, and nervous. I am excited that the first part of my treatment will be over. Happy because I anticipate this part was the most difficult. Nervous for what is to come.

I want to focus on the future and what that can bring. I am optimistic I will continue to do well with my treatment. I want to be a voice for those who will, unfortunately, come after me. My story will be shared because it needs to be told. Breast cancer can happen to anyone—it does not discriminate!—but with support from family and friends, it is doable. I know I have been surrounded by prayer; some people I do not even know pray for me. It has lifted me up knowing I have touched and meant something to each one of these people in my life.

I didn't know my strength, and I still don't understand how I got through these last three months without coming completely unglued. I had my moments for sure.

Faith and hope helped get me through, and so much LOVE. Love from all those who are so near and dear to me. The goodness of people has warmed my heart. I received a note and card from a friend the other day. Her words moved me: "You have been heavy on my heart." Sometimes, we touch people's lives in a way we are not even aware. I want to be that person who touches others with my story. I want to help others through their storm. I want to make a difference.

As I look toward tomorrow and my last chemo, I am hopeful.

Hopeful the cancer is gone and I will continue surviving.

Hopeful I will continue doing well with the next step, radiation.

Hopeful I can put other breast cancer patients at ease.

Hopeful my future will be bright and better than before.

March 30, 2018

Today is the day!

Today is my last day of chemo!

I made a poster the night before, marking the end of chemotherapy! It was therapeutic working on it. It was the end of such a very trying time in my life.

Thank You, God, for being my constant support. Thank You for giving me the strength to get through these last three months. I am blessed.

Thank you, Papa, for standing by my side and being that person I could feel with me.

Thank you to all the beautiful, special people who have been put in my life to support me. I so appreciate all who listened to me.

God is Good!

I went to my last chemo treatment and I recall all the committed staff I encountered that day. My oncologist. cheering me on, told me I had tolerated the chemo well. I made it! The phlebotomist who would draw my blood weekly praised me. The infusion nurse, whom I had grown to call my angel, was always calming, and today, so happy I was done. All of these people were such an integral part of my treatment. I will never forget them and will be eternally grateful for all they did for me and for all they continue to do for so many other cancer patients.

CHAPTER 15
ONTO RADIATION

The feeling of relief I felt after finishing chemotherapy was that of a giant weight lifted from my shoulders—three months of receiving chemotherapy once a week seemed like such a big mountain to climb. I am happy to say I got through it and I am ready to conquer the next mountain, radiation.

Before beginning radiation, I needed to get a CAT scan to determine where the cancer had been located. I then received tattoo marks (little blue dots) that helped align the radiation beams to target the exact area. The whole procedure was explained in great detail to me by a new doctor called a radiation oncologist. I brought my sister along for this appointment because I needed a second set of ears in case I missed any critical information. The radiation oncologist discussed the radiation procedure in clear terms. I was glad my sister was there because we could review everything after the appointment.

Because of my breast cancer location and larger breasts, it was explained that I had to receive my radiation lying on my stomach, with my breast exposed through a space on the table. Others may receive radiation while lying on their back. When you receive radiation treatment, the actual radiation time lasts only a few minutes, but the total time spent getting ready and positioned correctly takes twenty-to-forty-five minutes.

April 26, 2018

Almost a month done with chemo, and today is the start of radiation. I was tearful two days ago when I went for my simulation CAT scan and was marked with tattoo ink. These small pen-point tattoos will let the radiation techs know where to direct the radiation beams.

Today I am calm as I begin the second phase of my treatment for breast cancer. However, some apprehension has managed to creep into my mind. After today though, I will know what to expect. I will be driving myself and will continue to do so for the next four weeks. Radiation is five times a week, Monday through Friday. I will look at it as an essential job to go to and complete.

I am strong. I will get through this. I am wishing myself bright, beautiful, healing rays today.

May 3, 2018

I am finishing the first week of radiation. Physically, I am a little more fatigued. Emotionally, it has been difficult. Radiation has been challenging because of strangers' manual manipulation of my breast. One of them is a man. I know this is how it is done, but it feels mechanical and impersonal. When I enter the radiation treatment room, I need to immediately disrobe my top in front of two people and get onto this small, narrow table that has an open space in it. I line up my breast and place it in that space. Then the radiologist techs move and twist my breast and adjust me along with lining up my tattoos so I can receive radiation. The process, to me, is humiliating. I know I need to look at it as these rays heal me, but it isn't easy.

When I hear the machine go on and the ticking noise, I know the radiation is occurring and all I do is pray. I repeat the Hail Mary prayer over and over in my head until it is done.

God, give me the strength and courage to get through the following weeks. I need to stay strong and stay the course.

As I read this journal entry, I can still hear the ticking noise from the radiation machine. At times, it was upsetting, but reciting the Hail Mary gave me the comfort I needed. Chemotherapy and radiation were challenging, but I want you to know I felt confident that I was doing all I could do to help prevent a recurrence. I had to go through all the side effects and manipulation to get to the other side of treatment.

CHAPTER 16
KOMEN DETROIT RACE FOR THE CURE

One of the most joyous and significant days during my journey was attending the Komen Detroit Race for the Cure for the first time as a breast cancer survivor. I was still in treatment, receiving radiation, and my hair had started to grow back ever so slightly. I was so happy to be alive and support my pink sisters and myself at such an inspiring event. It had always been special as I'd helped plan the Race for the past four years.

This year was different and monumental. I had come full circle. I had experienced what it was like to be diagnosed, go through surgery and treatment, and come out on the other side of breast cancer. As I'd raised funds for the Race in all the previous years, I had no idea what those diagnosed with breast cancer went through. I knew this day would be memorable.

I was team captain of Get Your Pink On, and we had thirty team members. It was the biggest team I had ever had to date. They consisted of family, friends, and some of my husband's co-workers. I was in awe of all the support.

May 4, 2018

Tomorrow is the Komen Detroit Race for the Cure. It will be an emotional day for me on so many different levels. I now join the survival group. For the previous four years, I was the one supporting, fundraising, and cheering on those with breast cancer. Now I am the survivor. I am undergoing treatment, and this Race is about me and many others. I have always thought I could make a difference with my voice and the passion I have for this cause. I WILL make a difference.

I am being interviewed by a WXYZ news reporter tomorrow morning at the Race. I don't know what she will ask, but I know what I want to make clear: Get your yearly mammogram. Don't put it off. My breast cancer was found on my annual mammogram. If I can convince one woman to go get that mammogram they have been putting off and possibly save a life, I have done my job and made a difference!

To a bright, beautiful day tomorrow.

May all my days moving forward be positive and filled with hope, peace, and love.

I am a fighter.

I will get through all of this and become a better person. I can feel it from deep inside me.

May 6, 2018

I am beaming in the afterglow of the 27th Annual Komen Detroit Race for the Cure, which was yesterday. What a day! I was interviewed by a reporter from WXYZ, Channel 7, in the early morning. It was 6:30 a.m. I knew I wanted to stress that breast cancer can happen to anyone and the importance of yearly mammograms. Everything went well, and I was so thankful for my neighbors Pete and Jami for getting up so early to join Jim and me during the interview.

It was a beautiful day filled with such great support. It meant so much that my brother, John, was there with his wife, Karen, to be part of my team. It meant even more when I read the pink sign attached to his back, "I Race in Celebration of My Little Sister Josephine". It brought tears to my eyes.

My team consisted of thirty members. Jim's family was so supportive. His mom, Carol, his brother, Eric, my sister-in-law, Michelle, and family friends, Bill, Kristine, and Dan, came to support me. Jim's co-workers, Klara and Ana, also joined us for the Race. All who participated and walked alongside me left a lasting impression. There was my friend, Yvette, who came with her husband and son. My friend, Kim, a breast cancer survivor, came with her husband to be part of my team. My friend from PA school, Brandy, came with her daughter and son, Alyssa and Joey. My friends, Carla and Tabitha, who was another breast cancer survivor, and Tabitha's daughter walked with us. Friends of friends joined my team. I was proud to say there were five survivors in total. Walking together on this day with all my pink sisters, I could feel the sisterhood and knew I would never be alone.

Being on stage during Opening Ceremonies, holding the under-one-year survivor sign as part of the Honor Guard, was very moving. The woman standing next to me with metastatic breast cancer profoundly affected me. It was emotional seeing her tears and the tears from all of her friends in the crowd. It made me realize the preciousness of life.

God gave us a glorious, sunny day. It gave me HOPE.

The Komen Detroit Race for the Cure is something you need to experience to understand the depths of all it represents. After being diagnosed, I recalled all the survivors wearing their pink shirts on Race day. It gave me HOPE that I would be okay and that everything I was about to face was doable. That HOPE was priceless to my recovery.

Jim and me at the 2019 Komen Detroit Race for the Cure

Some of my Race Team, Get Your Pink On (2018)

CHAPTER 17
HEALTHY LIFESTYLE CHOICES

As I neared the end of radiation, I began thinking about healthy lifestyle choices. I questioned if there was something I unintentionally had done to cause my breast cancer. After much reflection, I concluded that there was nothing I had done; however, the thought of recurrence continually looms in the back of my mind. I began thinking about how I could live a healthier lifestyle to help prevent that recurrence. I have to admit, I became somewhat obsessed with the search to achieve better health. But what a great obsession!

First, I took a look at the products I was using on my body. These included hair products, skincare products, makeup, deodorants, soaps, and lotions. I began reading ingredient labels more carefully. I changed everything to paraben-free. Parabens are added to personal care products as a preservative, allowing products to have a longer shelf life. "Parabens are known endocrine disruptors that can mimic estrogen in the body. Several studies have shown that parabens can affect the mechanisms of normal breast cells and potentially influence their abnormal growth, leading to increased risk for breast cancer."[3] After reading up on parabens, I knew I did not want to continue using products containing them.

Next, I looked at my exercise regimen, which was almost nonexistent except for my walks. I love walking, especially outdoors, surrounded by nature and inhaling the fresh air. I knew I needed improvement in this area of my life. I reached out to my neighbor, Jami, a Pilates instructor, and set out on an exercise program with her. It made me feel so much better. My muscles were getting stronger and I was committed to the workouts three-to-four times a week. I continued working on my cardiovascular exercise as well. Studies show that regular cardiovascular exercise, at least one hundred fifty minutes a week, may help lower your risk of getting breast cancer. Along with exercise, I also limit my alcohol intake and I do not smoke.

The next aspect of my life I knew I had to change was my diet. One day, I was talking to my friend Anissa, who recommended an integrative medicine oncologist, Dr. Sheba Roy. Integrative oncology utilizes natural medicine therapies. For me, these include supplements along with building a healthy nutrition plan. Dr. Roy's goal is to meet both the patient's and the provider's needs by being a trustworthy liaison between conventional management and complementary care. Dr. Roy, along with her associate, Dr. March, treated my whole being, including addressing the emotional trauma associated with a cancer diagnosis. After an initial consultation with Dr. Roy, comprised of a detailed health history and bloodwork, a program specific to my healthcare needs was designed. These remarkable physicians are empathetic, extremely knowledgeable, and genuinely care about helping you achieve optimal health.

Changing my eating habits made a significant difference. I had more energy and slept better after making the changes suggested. It took a while to get to where I am today with my diet. Dr. March helped me gradually change how and what I ate daily. I reduced the number of animal products I consume and eat a more plant-based diet, consisting of organic fruits and vegetables. I enjoy eating an array of colorful fruits and vegetables, especially those in season. I take pleasure in experimenting with a variety of vegetarian recipes.

Along with diet and exercise, I continue improving my mind and spirit. Meditation continues to be an integral part of my life. During treatment, I meditated twice daily. The meditations calmed me and helped me to focus. Sometimes I used a visualization meditation, concentrating on healing my body; other times, I meditated for relaxation. This helped improve my physical and emotional well-being. Additionally, daily prayer keeps me grounded. I have a strong faith, and knowing I could talk to God at any time during my journey gave me great comfort. Prayer continues to be an important part of my daily life.

Incorporating these lifestyle changes, along with improving my mind and spirit, have greatly enhanced my overall health. I know there are no guarantees in life, but I have now taken control to a healthier life, hopefully preventing many types of disease, not just cancer. It is a positive win for me anyway I look at it.

CHAPTER 18
BEGINNING TAMOXIFEN AND ENDING RADIATION

Tamoxifen was on my mind as I knew my oncologist would soon prescribe it. Every step of this journey was frightening, and introducing a new drug into my body was daunting. I had researched Tamoxifen online and I had my reservations. The side effects were not pleasant. I worried about hot flashes and weight gain. Reading about the rare side effects of blood clots and uterine cancer made me uneasy. I had joined a Facebook group for women on Tamoxifen. Some of the posts worried me, especially the side effects. These Facebook groups have their downfalls. At times, reading the posts was depressing, but on the other hand, I found specific posts informative and helpful. You have to just read through it and decide what is pertinent and most beneficial to you. After a lengthy conversation with my oncologist, I did decide to go on Tamoxifen. He convinced me it was in my best interest to take it.

May 9, 2018

With much trepidation, I started Tamoxifen today. I know this revolutionary drug will decrease my chances of breast cancer recurrence, but I am afraid of the potential side effects. Ultimately, the benefits outweigh the risks for me. I will take it and pray for minimal side effects, if any at all. I will need to be on Tamoxifen for five-to-ten years.

I am getting closer to the end of this journey with radiation and Herceptin infusions.

God, bless me with continued good health.

I am fortunate. So far, there are minimal side effects from the Tamoxifen. I have difficulty losing weight and have intermittent joint pain. Each person experiences different side effects. As I speak with others, I learn what they are going through. I am lucky I do not have the fatigue that many complain they experience. As one door opens to a new treatment, the addition of Tamoxifen, I am happy to say another door closes. No more radiation.

May 24, 2018

LAST DAY OF RADIATION!

I am thrilled to have another part of this journey behind me.

I have to say, I was not too fond of radiation. It was violating to me. I did not like men touching, pulling, and repositioning my breast. I know it is part of their job, but I did not like it.

I had fewer side effects with radiation than with chemotherapy. I experienced some cracking of the skin under my breast. I also had skin peeling under my armpit toward the end of my radiation treatment. I did use the creams recommended faithfully, and I know that helped.

A celebration is in order. I am thankful I am getting through all of these treatments. You never know how strong you are until you are faced with and conquer something like breast cancer.

May 25, 2018

It was a bit of an emotional day for me yesterday as I had my last radiation treatment. I completed chemo and radiation. Now just a Herceptin infusion every three weeks until the end of the year.

I went for a walk this morning. As I walked through my neighborhood before my last treatment, I welcomed the sun on this spring day. As I tilted my head back, I felt the sun's warmth on my face. It was a wonderful feeling. I had my earbuds in, listening to Whitney Houston songs as I walked. One song was about God and the other was about strength. Music got me through some of the rough days. The song I listened to says, "I didn't know my own strength." When a diagnosis like breast cancer comes along, it brings you to your knees. I got up and fought.

As I went to my last radiation treatment, all the staff, including the receptionists, radiologist techs, nurses, and doctors, congratulated me. The radiation oncologist told me I had done very well. He said my skin irritations would improve with time.

Jim made my last day of treatment very special. It started with kind, encouraging words in the morning and a meaningful card. Then, when I returned home, there was a gorgeous bouquet of pink and white flowers waiting for me. We finished the day with a nice dinner out.

What does this journey mean to me and the life that is now ahead of me? What will the new me look like? Who will she be?

CHAPTER 19
THE NEW ME

With treatment behind me, I felt a new lease on life. I was excited to see what life had in store for me. I was thankful that maintaining a positive attitude through my cancer journey had immensely helped my recovery. Don't get me wrong, there were days I did not know how I would make it through. Remarkably, I fought cancer and conquered the beast that affects so many. The lessons learned along the way will leave me changed forever. I certainly have an all-new appreciation for life and its fragility.

As I wrote this book, I reflected on my journal entries daily. It was a cathartic experience reliving this journey. I hope it has helped you, the reader. As I return and read one of the last entries in my cancer journal one year after my initial diagnosis, my words are clear and my outlook is good.

October 12, 2018

> One year ago today, I was diagnosed with breast cancer. At times I really cannot believe how I got through everything. I realized that family, friends, Komen, and Karmanos all played a vital part in my treatment and recovery. Everyone made me feel at ease, especially on the dark days.

> I know I am not done with the journey, but I am optimistic the journey will be less bumpy. This day, one year ago, is so pronounced in my memory. Jim and I were starting a short trip to Petoskey when I received the phone call that would change the next year of my life.

Staring your mortality in the face makes you realize the preciousness of life. Even though I am finished with treatment, that does not mean I am done with cancer. I cannot push cancer or my experience out of my mind. It is always there. It is woven into who I am.

I thank God for giving me the strength on the days I could not bear one more thing. I thank my dad for always watching over me as my guardian angel. Within this trying time of my life, I learned that your mother will always be your mother, no matter what health issues she may have or the pain she endures. I see the love in my mother's eyes. The way she wants to help me and all her kind words of encouragement have meant so much. My love for her is infinite, and that love has helped me through this year.

I learned this past year what I mean to people. I will never question that I am loved and that people care about me. The most special bond became stronger this past year with my friend Carla. She has stood by me through cancer and some of the most-difficult challenges in my life. She was my sounding board countless times. How fortunate I am to have a longtime loyal friend like Carla. Such strong women were placed in my life. I am grateful for every one of them. I believe I will join them, for, without strength, this road traveled would have been less manageable.

Many things came to mind while I was going through my journey. I learned the importance of being your own advocate from a healthcare perspective. Be sure to speak up when you have questions and ask for explanations. You have choices, and always keep in mind that you help manage your healthcare to a certain extent. Value all the professionals brought into your life and understand that they are the experts in their area of practice.

After a year of being in treatment, I reassessed my life. I learned to seize opportunities and not put off my dreams, take the trip I have been putting off, take risks in my professional life. I learned the importance of bringing joy to those around me. Make sure to take time out for your family and friends, and visit them whether they live near or far. Tell those in your life what they mean to you, and be sure to appreciate the little things. Yes, a new lease on life certainly puts things into perspective.

Looking back, I wrote that one of the most-traumatic events during my journey was losing my hair. I am happy to say it grew back beautifully, a shiny salt-and-pepper color. I have never received as many compliments on my hair as I do today. My new hair is another silver lining of my cancer journey. I now look at myself in the mirror and know who is staring back at me. That woman is strong and can withstand much more than she ever imagined.

RESOURCE GUIDE

Breast Cancer Resources

- **American Cancer Society**
  www.cancer.org

- **Breast and Cervical Cancer Control Program (BCCCP)**
  Karmanos Cancer Institute
  www.bcccp.org
  888-242-2702

- **Metastatic Breast Cancer Alliance (MBCalliance)**
  www.mbcalliance.org

- **Susan G. Komen**
  www.komen.org
  1-877-GO KOMEN (1-877-465-6636)
  Email: Helpline@komen.org

Comprehensive Cancer Centers in Michigan

- **Karmanos Cancer Institute**
  www.karmanos.org
  1-800-KARMANOS (1-800-572-6266)

- **Rogel Cancer Center**
  University of Michigan Health
  www.rogelcancercenter.org
  800-865-1125

Integrative Medicine

- **Associates of Integrative Medicine**
  Sheba Roy, ND, FABNO
  www.aimnatural.com
  248-798-2942

Cancer Support Systems

- **Cancer Support Services**
  CSS Hotline 888-793-9355

- **Gilda's Club Metro Detroit**
  www.glidasclubdetroit.org
  248-577-0800
  Email: gildasclubdetroit.org

Cancer Support Community

- **Gilda's Club**
  www.cancersupportcommuity.org/cancer-support-helpline
  888-793-9355

- **Sisters Network Inc.**
  www.sistersnetworkinc.org
  866-781-1808
  Email: infonet@sistersnetworkinc.org

- **Young Survival Coalition**
  www.youngsurvival.org
  877-972-1011
  Email: support@youngsurvival.org

Financial Resources

- **My Sistah's Pink Journey**
  https://mspjourney.org
  313-405-9056

- **New Day Foundation for Families**
  www.foundationforfamilies.org
  248-648-1105

- **The Pink Fund**
  https://pinkfund.org
  877-234-PINK (7465)

- **Shades of Pink Foundation**
  www.shadesofpinkfoundation.org
  248-320-1559

REFERENCES

[1] Giridhar, K. M. D. (n.d.). *HER2-positive breast cancer: What is it?* Retrieved from: https://www.mayoclinic.org/breast-cancer/expert-answers/faq-20058066

[2] Co-survivor. Susan G. Komen®. (2021, November 25). Retrieved from: https://www.komen.org/support-resources/support/for-friends-and-family/for-co-survivors/

[3] *Parabens.* Breast Cancer Prevention Partners (BCPP). (2021, August 18). Retrieved from: https://www.bcpp.org/resource/parabens/

ABOUT THE AUTHOR

Josephine Roach is a leader in the breast cancer community. She serves as Chairperson of the Detroit Komen Leadership Council and is a member of the Komen Detroit Race for the Cure Planning Committee. She is a member of the Karmanos Cancer Advocacy Program (KCAP) and is the founder of the Facebook breast cancer support group, Where HOPE Begins. Breast cancer advocacy is her passion, focusing on education and awareness. She has been honored with numerous awards for her service in the breast cancer community.

 Josephine received her Bachelor of Arts in Communication Disorders and Sciences from Wayne State University in Detroit and her Master of Science in Physician Assistant Studies from the University of Detroit Mercy. She resides in Southeast Michigan with her husband Jim, where they share hobbies of travel, bird watching, and classic cars.

To Contact Josephine Roach:

Email: josephineroach11@gmail.com
Website: https://journeywithjosephine.now.site/
Facebook: www.facebook.com/jo.ri.127
Instagram: www.instagram.com/josephineroachsurvivor/
LinkedIn: www.linkedin.com/in/josephine-roach-8425531b3

Made in the USA
Columbia, SC
27 August 2022

65759647R00061